Back to Basics

ENGLISH

for 6-7 year olds

BOOK ONE

Sheila Lane and Marion Kemp

There are 26 letters in the alphabet.

Write over the small letters and the capital letters.

Fill in the missing letters.

Colour the odd one out.

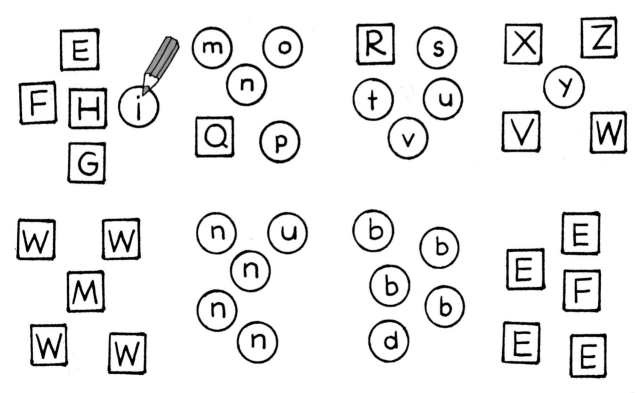

Letters make sounds.
Sounds make words.

Say the sound made by the first letter
of each word.

r for ring   a for apple   t for tree

r a t   is rat

That's me!

Write the first letter of each
word and say the sound.

Write the word
the sounds make.

4

Write the first letter and say the sound.

Draw the picture and write the word.

is

is

is

is

is

is

Read the sentences.　　Write the sentence to match the picture.

 This is an apple.

This is a ball.

<u>This is a ball.</u>

 This is a bus.

This is a car.

_____.

 This is a kite.

This is a balloon.

_____.

 This is a jug.

This is a cup.

_____.

 This is a banana.

This is the moon.

_____.

Read the words
in the balloon.

Write the words in
sentences.

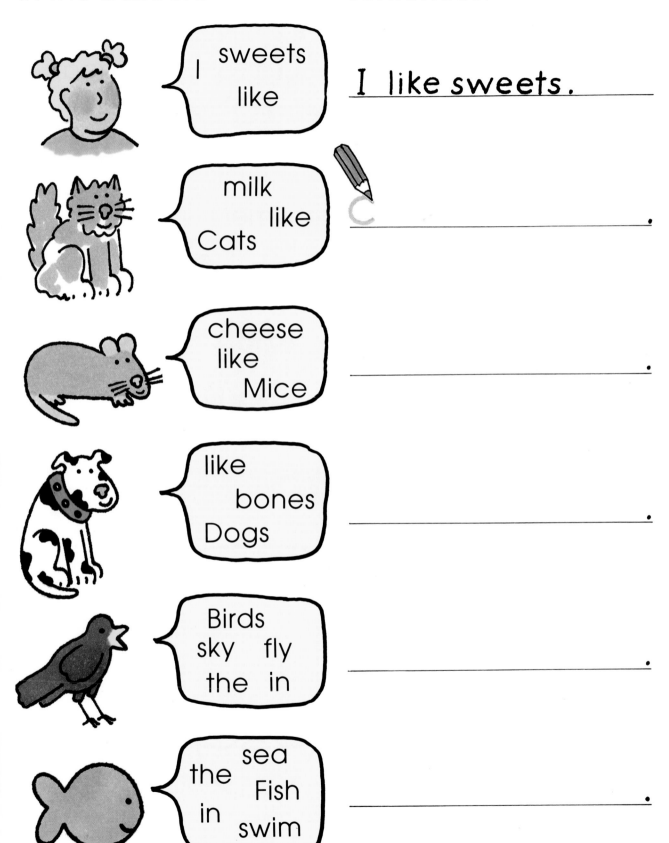

I sweets like

I like sweets.

milk like Cats

_____.

cheese like Mice

_____.

like bones Dogs

_____.

Birds sky fly the in

_____.

the sea Fish in swim

_____.

Some words make rhymes.

Words which have the same sound at the end are called rhymes.

a goat
in
a boat

Write over the words that rhyme and finish the pictures.

a **mouse**
on
a **house**

a hat
on
a cat

a ball
on
a wall

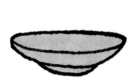

a fish
on
a dish

a ring
on
a string

a flag
on
a bag

8

Say   Say

in bin win can

in
bin
win

Write the three words that rhyme.

at   at sat cup fat

it   it dog bit sit

an   an ran cot man

me   me we be rug

and   and look sand band

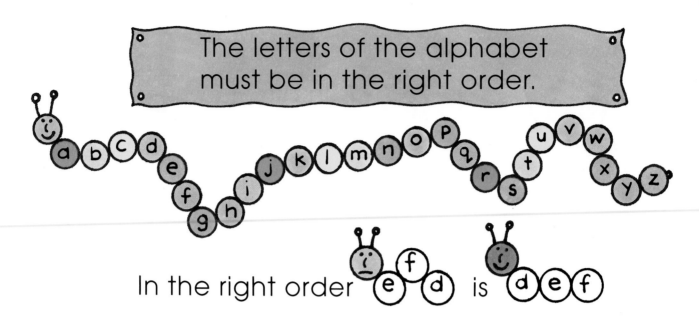

The letters of the alphabet must be in the right order.

In the right order $ef d$ is def

Write the letters in the right order.

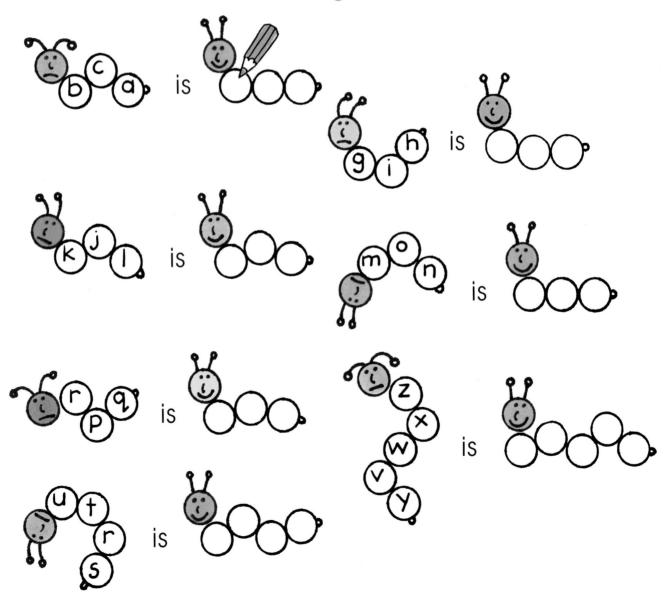

Colour in the words you can make from the letters in my name.

caterpillar

at   dog   ill   to   mug
cat   zoo   car   rat   pet

Try my name!

rabbit

at   on   cut   bar   rat
pig   bat   bit   it   egg

Try my name!

penguin

up   cap   in   cup   pen
pin   peg   gun   and   the

Try my name!

leopard

do   cow   pad   sun   rod
for   lad   are   hen   pod

11

Letters make sounds.
Sounds make words.

Write the first letter
and say the sound.

Draw the picture
and write the word.

s w a n   is **swan**

f __ __ __   is _____

__ __ __ __   is _____

__ __ __ __   is _____

12

Write the first letter of each word.

G o   t o   b e d

Write the sentence.   Go to bed.

___ ___ ___ ___

___ ___ ___ ___

___ ___ ___

Some words make rhymes.

Say the words.
Draw a (ring) round
the word that
does **not** rhyme.

car

star

book

jar

hen

owl

10 ten

pen

bee

tree

3 three

6 six

boat

coat

egg

goat

moon

ring

king

wing

14

Write a new word to
make a rhyme and
draw the picture.

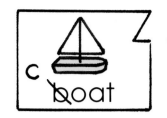 

c b̶oat   coat

   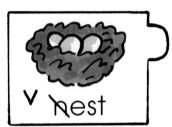 

s b̶un   s   p b̶ear

b h̶ook   v n̶est

Make a rhyme for:

tree	rat	hit	pen
me	mat	lit	when
he	that	pit	hen
see	_____	_____	_____

sing	fly	ice	day
ping	try	rice	play
wing	by	nice	way
_____	_____	_____	_____

15

Look at the picture.

six
eggs

a pot
of jam

a bag
of
apples

Go to the shops
and buy . . .

a loaf
of
bread

a bar
of
chocolate

What did you buy?
Put a tick ✓ or a cross ✗

a bar
of
chocolate ✓

a bag
of
jam ✗

a loaf
of
bread

six
eggs

a pot
of
eggs

a bar of
apples

a loaf
of
chocolate

a pot
of
jam

six
bread

a bag
of
apples

16

Look at the
set of pictures.

They are all sweets.

numbers   colours   letters   toys   books

Write a sentence for each set.

They are all _____   They _____

They _____

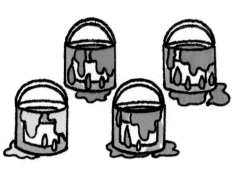

They _____   They _____

Sentences can tell a story.

Read the picture story.

The Giant _____

_____

_____   _____

_____   _____

_____   _____

Write the right sentence under each picture.

The Giant took little Tom to his castle.
Tom sat on a cotton reel.
He had a thimble for a cup.
Tom went to bed in a matchbox.

Sentences can ask riddles.

Look at the pictures.   Read the sentences.

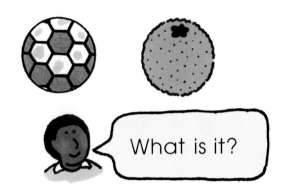

It is round.
You can eat it.
It begins with letter o.

It is an orange

It is hot.
It is in the sky.
It begins with letter s.

_____

It has four legs.
It drinks milk.
It begins with letter c.

_____

It is white.
It comes from a cow.
It begins with letter m.

_____

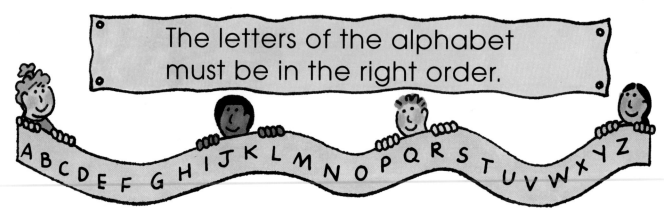

The letters of the alphabet must be in the right order.

A B C D E F G H I J K L M N O P Q R S T U V W X Y Z

Who comes first in the right order?

In the right order

is Ann Ben Colin

Write the names in the right order.

Bob Carol Amy   is [ ] [ ] [ ]

Kate Mary Leroy   is [ ] [ ] [ ]

Gina Fred Eric   is [ ] [ ] [ ]

Harry Ian June is [ ] [ ] [ ]

Tom Sam Ray   is [ ] [ ] [ ]

Colour in the words you can make with the letters in my name.
Elizabeth

he | up | let | you | the | lit | go | heel

name | bee | at | bath | zoo | bet | go

Find some more words.
Write them here.

Try my name.
Christopher

sit | that | ship | pot | her | post

shut | good | cold | vest | she | cot

Find some more words.
Write them here.

A sentence must make sense.

Draw lines so that each sentence makes sense.

Write the sensible sentence.

 Cows   lay eggs

 Hens   give milk

<u>Cows give milk.</u>

<u>Hens lay eggs.</u>

 I hear   with my eyes

 I see   with my ears

_____

_____

 Cats have   two legs

 I have   four legs

_____

_____

 Bees can   hop

 Frogs can   sting

_____

_____

Ducks can   bark

Dogs can   quack

_____

_____

Sentences can ask riddles.

Look at the pictures.

Read the sentences.

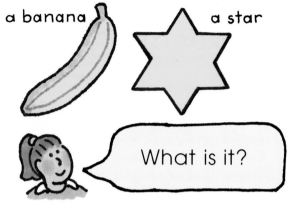

It is yellow.
It is in the sky at night.
You cannot eat it.
<u>It is a star.</u>

It is slow.
It has a house on its back.
It has four legs.

_____

It can fly in the sky.
It has wings.
It makes a nest in a tree.

_____

It has a face.
It does not have eyes.
It has hands but no legs.

_____

Sometimes two letters can go together to make one sound.

Say  shop | s⟩⟨h makes a s⟩⟨h sound

Draw a ring round the (sh) sounds in these words:

Write the words on the sheet.

 shut   shot   shell
wish   crash   smash

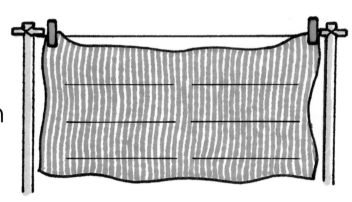

Say church | c⟩⟨h makes a c⟩⟨h sound

Draw a ring round the (ch) sounds in these words:

Write the words in the chain.

chip   chop   cheese
rich   lunch   pinch

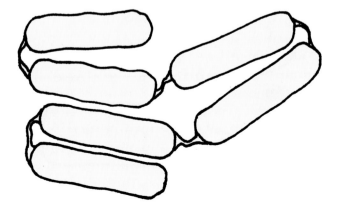

Write sh or ch at the beginning of each word.

_ _air _ _ip _ _ick _ _oe _ _urch

Write sh or ch at the end of each word.

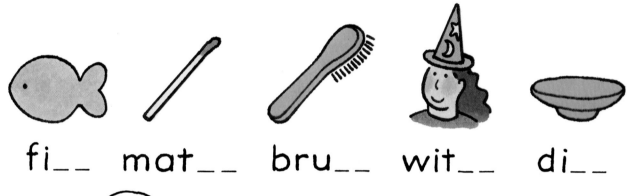

fi_ _ mat_ _ bru_ _ wit_ _ di_ _

Draw a (ring) round the right words.

I wear choose
        shoes on my feet.

The shop
     chop door is open.

Ships
Chips sail on the sea.

We will go to the football crash.
                           match.

It's wish and chips for punch.
      fish   ships   lunch.

Read the names of the shapes.

circle   square   triangle   rectangle   oval

Read the sentences.   Make a funny face.

1 Draw an oval shape
   for a face.

2 Draw a rectangle
   for a hat.

3 Put two little
   triangles for ears.

4 Add more shapes.

1 Draw a square
   for a face.

2 Draw a triangle
   for a hat.

3 Draw two little
   circles for ears.

4 Add more shapes.

Read the sentences.

I ate the cake.
I made a cake.
I cooked the cake.

Write the sentences in the right order.

I made _____.

I _____.

I _____.

I opened the box.
Out jumped a pet mouse.
I picked up the box.

_____.

_____.

_____.

A sentence must make sense.

This is a sentence: Did you see the clown? ✓

This is not a sentence: the clown ✗

Tick ✓ the words that make a sentence.

 Can you read?   Do you like jam?
Can you   Do you

A sweet   A cat's fur
Give me a sweet.   A cat's fur is soft.

Draw lines so that each sentence makes sense.

 A baby sheep  is called a puppy.

 A baby dog   is called a kitten.

A baby cat   is called a lamb.

A boy has   four wheels.

 A car has   four legs.

 A mouse has   two legs.

tortoise A shell
has a

A tortoise has a shell.

bird has A wings

camel hump
has A a

giraffe has long
a A neck

donkey A has
ears long

elephant has
a An trunk

Write the new word and draw the picture.

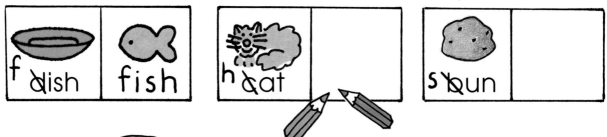

Draw a (ring) round the word that does **not** rhyme in each set.

see
he we
go

sat
up fat
pat

the
look book
took

Draw lines so that each sentence makes sense.

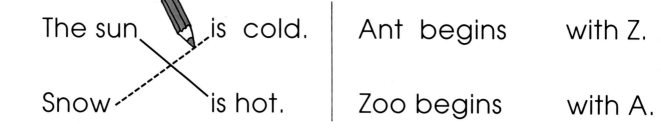

The sun   is cold.   Ant begins   with Z.

Snow   is hot.   Zoo begins   with A.

I have   four legs.   Two and two   make six.

Dogs have   two legs.   Three and three make fou

Draw a (ring) round the right word in each sentence.

Chops

Ships   sail on the sea.

Shut

Chat   the door please.

shell.

An egg has a

chin.

Write the words in sensible sentences.

An
is big
elephant   **An elephant is big.**

mouse
A little
is   _____.

A has
zebra
stripes   _____.

leopard
A spots
has   _____.

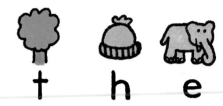 Can you get the message?

Write the first letters
and make words like this:

 t h e

_____   _____

_____   _____

_____   _____

_____   _____

_____   _____

Write the message. _____

_____

_____

_____